WHIZZ KIDZ
Brain Puzzles

ARCTURUS

This edition published in 2019 by Arcturus Publishing Limited
26/27 Bickels Yard, 151–153 Bermondsey Street,
London SE1 3HA

Written by: William Potter
Illustrated by: Matthew Scott
Designed by: Well Nice
Cover design by: Ms Mousepenny
Edited by: Sebastian Rydberg

ISBN: 978-1-78950-310-4
CH007013NT
Supplier 33, Date 0819, Print run 8574

Printed in China

Butterfly Chain

The pattern on this butterfly's wings changes one step at a time.
Fill in the large butterfly, so that it is number 6 in the sequence.

1   2   3   4   5

6

Cookie Crumbs

A large cookie has been cut into pieces.
Which four shapes fit together to complete
the cookie in the circle?

2

7

1

5

3

4

6

Clever Cube

Which unfolded cube plan matches the animal cube
at the bottom right?

A

B

C

Super Skyline

Put the pieces of sky in the right order from left to right, so that they fit above the hero's city skyline.

A B C D E F G H I J K L

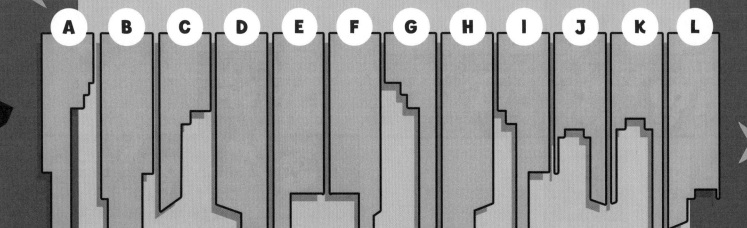

F C ....

Fit the Fish

Where do the fishy squares fit in the grid to complete the picture? Write each number in the square where it belongs.

1 **2** **3** **4**

Fruit Salad

Copy the fruit into the empty squares, so that each fruit
appears just once in every row, column,
and group of nine squares.

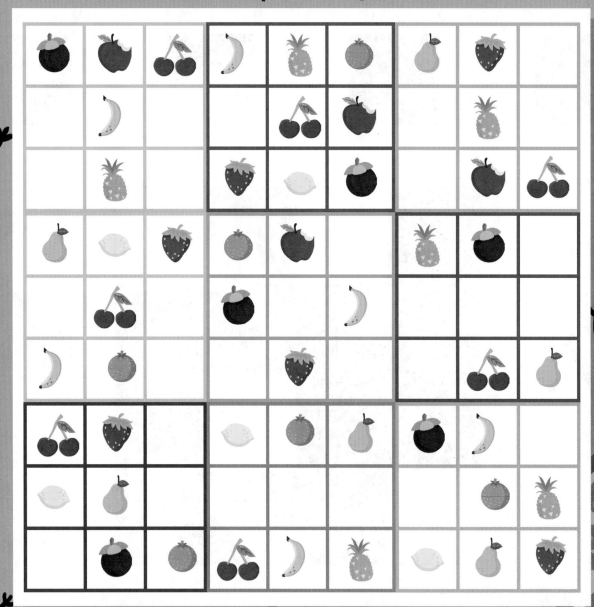

Farm Fencing

Draw just three straight lines across the field to put each animal in its own separate area.

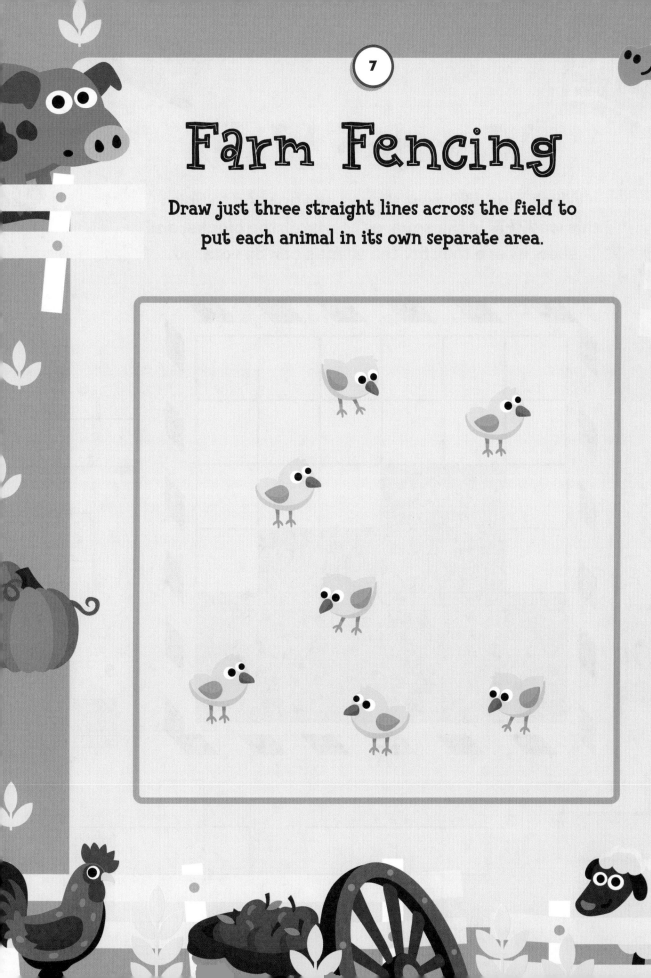

Wonder Wall

Which four different shapes can be used to finish this wall? Fill in the squares to match the blocks, and show where they fit. The shapes can be rotated.

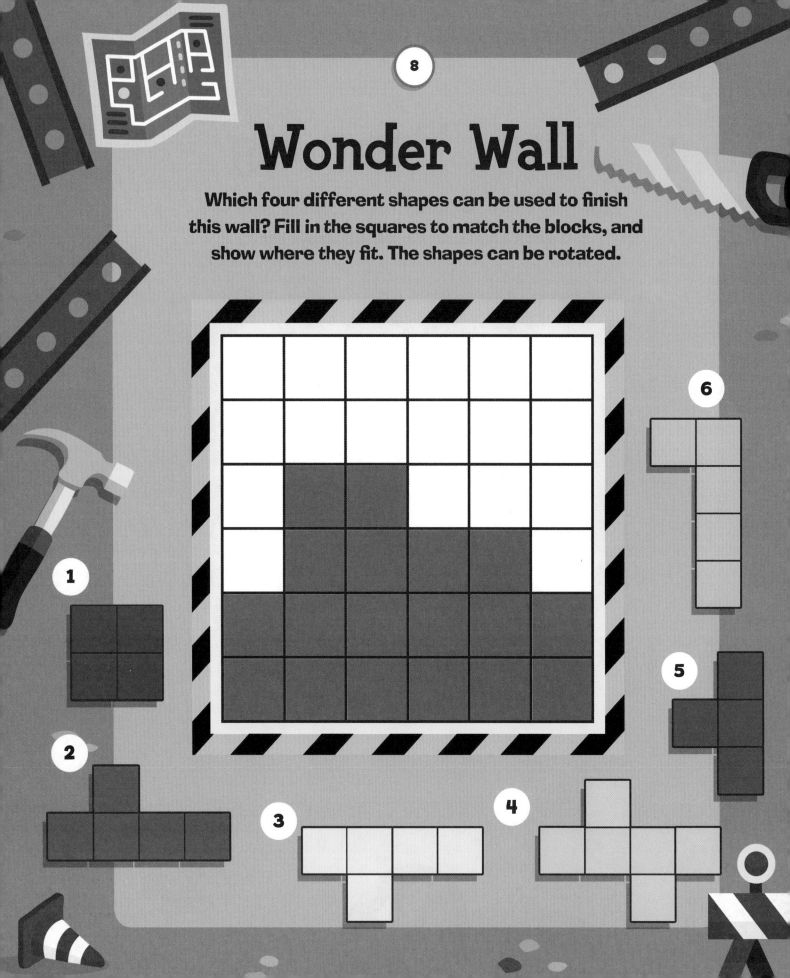

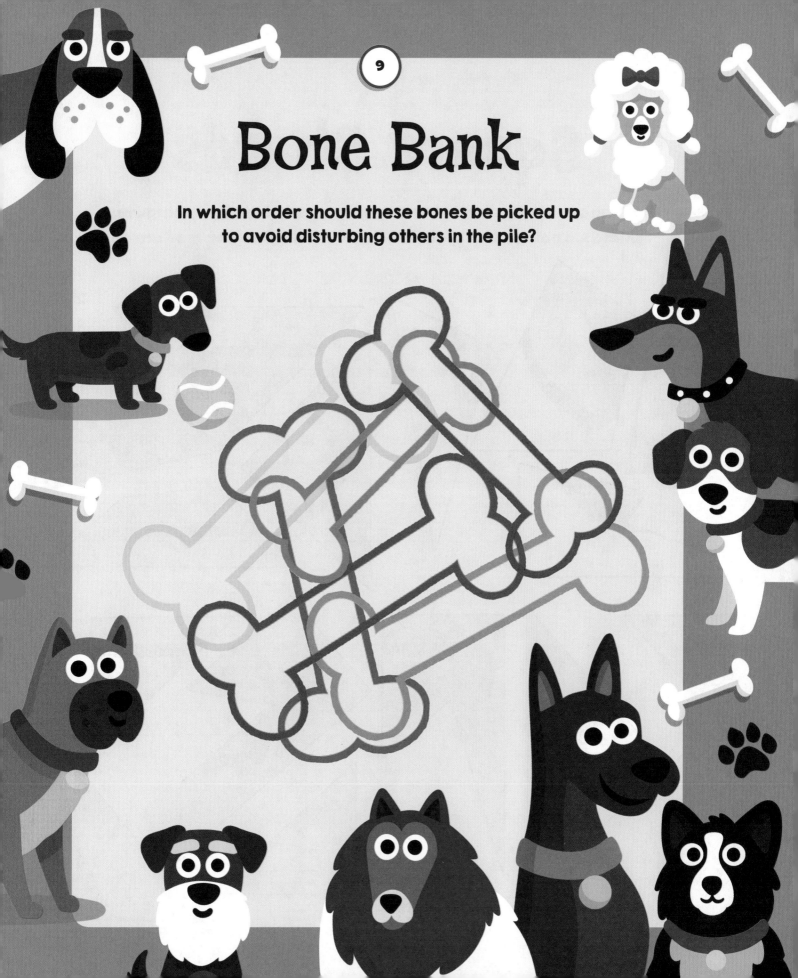

Bone Bank

In which order should these bones be picked up to avoid disturbing others in the pile?

Square Shards

Sir Dancealot has been testing his sword skills by slicing four shields. Look at the pieces. Which shield was not a square?

1

2

3

4

Planet Path

Plot a course for the rocket to visit all of the green planets. Connect all the green worlds with straight lines, without crossing your path or any red planets.

Start

Chop, Chop!

How many red pepper slices has the chef put in the frying pan?

Super Sleuth

Do you have the skills to be a top detective? Look carefully at the collection of clues for one minute, then turn the page to answer the questions.

Super Sleuth

**Without turning back to the last page,
try answering these questions:**

1. What was the time on the clock?

2. Did the socks have spots or stripes?

3. What did the dog have around its neck?

4. Where was the key hidden?

5. How many books were removed from the shelf?

6. What did the photograph show?

7. Which fruits were left uneaten?

8. What activity is the boot used for?

Party Path

Each vehicle has its own start and directions to follow.
Which one finds its way to the party, marked 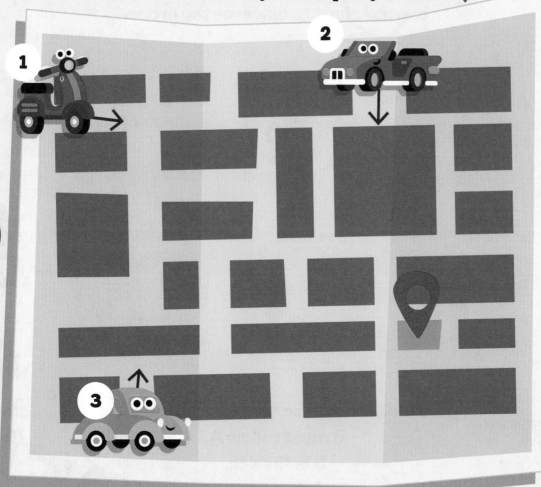?

1
Take 1st right, 2nd left,
1st left, 1st right,
2nd right, 1st right,
2nd left, 1st right.

2
Take 1st right, 3rd left,
2nd right, 1st left,
1st left, 2nd right,
1st left, 2nd left.

3
Take 1st right, 1st left,
2nd left, 1st right,
2nd right, 3rd right,
1st right, 1st left.

Break-In

To open the safe and reach the valuables,
the thief must open the locks in order.
Use the clues to discover the order.

A **B** **C**

D **E** **F**

The locks should be opened in this order:
B must follow A,
D is the 4th,
C follows F,
D is before A,
E is not first.

....

Trick Shot

If the basketball bounces off walls at 90 degrees, where does it end?

Start

A

B

C

D

Fashion First

The total price for each row and column is shown on the right and bottom of the grid. Work out how much each item is worth. One answer has been given to you already.

Mat Match

Which group of squares cannot be found on
the picnic mat, even when it is rotated?

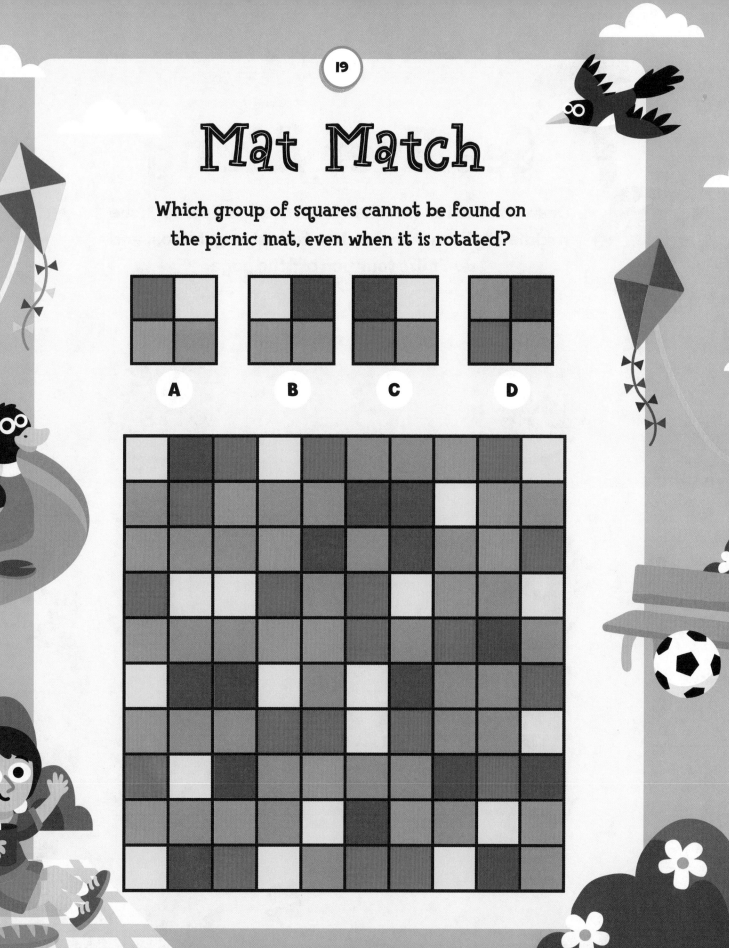

A   B   C   D

See Everything

Draw a route for the hiker from the start through the middle of all nine circles. Use four straight lines, and don't lift your pen off the page.

Start

Freaky Face

Fill in the squares on the right side of the grid to complete a symmetrical Frankenstein's monster face.

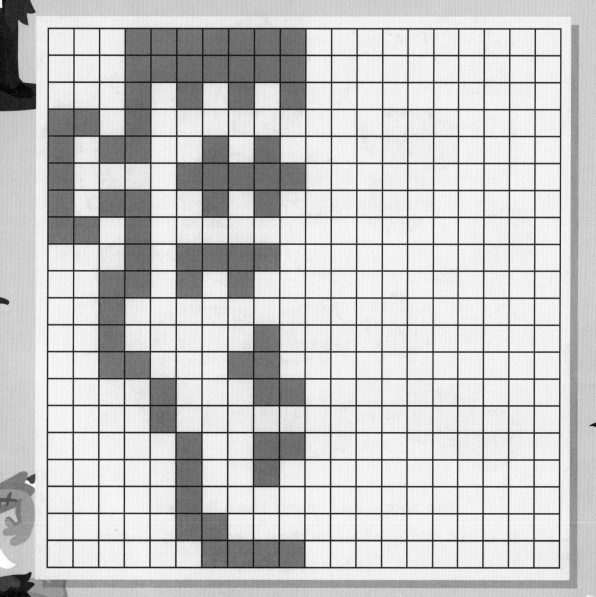

Sweet Pick

Which shape is being described from this collection of candies?

The shape has fewer than 8 sides.
It is in a group of more than 2 touching shapes.
It is not green.
It has more than 4 sides.
It is touching a shape with a higher number of sides.

Turning Time

Each cog turns in the opposite direction of the cog next to it. Which way will the red cog turn?

Break the Code

Use the code cracker to help the spies decipher the secret message.

ONE OF YOUR AGENTS IS A SPY FOR THE OTHER SIDE

A	B	C	D	E	F	G	H	I	J	K	L	M

N	O	P	Q	R	S	T	U	V	W	X	Y	Z

Hats Off

How many times does the word HAT appear in a straight line in the grid forward, backward, across, up, down, or diagonally?

H	A	T	T	H
A	A	H	A	H
T	H	T	A	H
A	T	A	H	A
H	A	H	A	T

Hit the Beat

These seven drumsticks form one large triangle. How would you move two drumsticks to make three equal-sized triangles?

Solutions

1

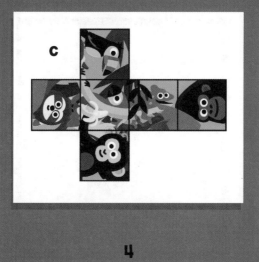

The patterns on the large spots move one step at a time, from the middle to the outer ring. The small spots and the background of the wings swap between green and pink.

2

3

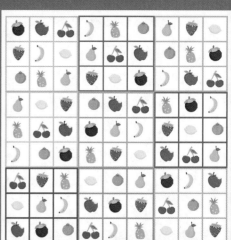

C

4

F, C, I, A, G, L, B, J, D, H, K, E

5

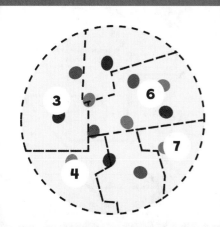

6

7

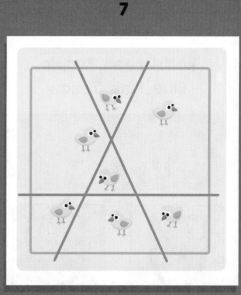

8

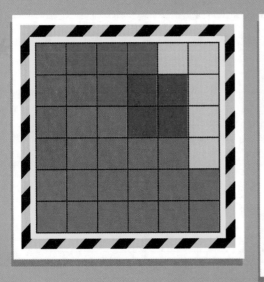

11

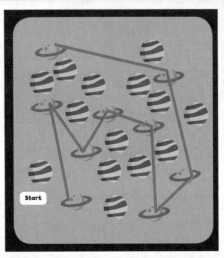

Start

15

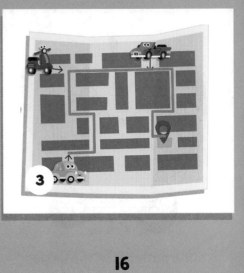

3

9

Red, Green, Purple,
Blue, Pink, Yellow

12

14

16

F, C, E, D, A, B

17

10

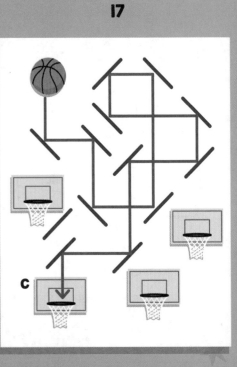

4

C

13-14

1. 2:30
2. Stripes
3. A blue collar
4. On the book shelf
5. 3
6. A mountain
7. A banana, a strawberry
8. Ice skating

18

4

8

6

9

20

Reflections and rotations are also valid answers.

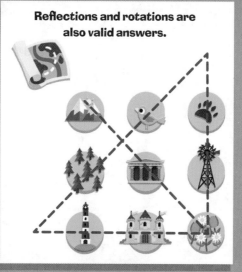

22

23

19

C

21

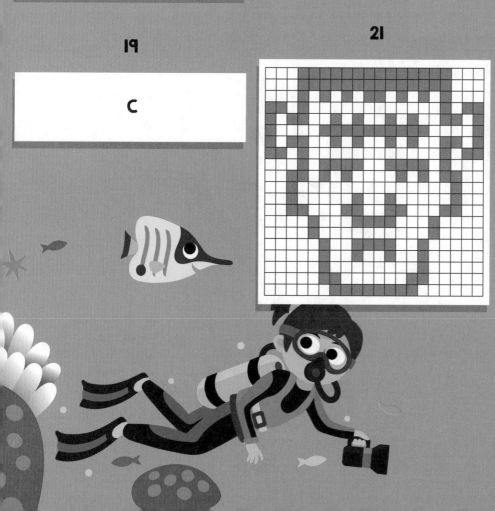

24

One of your agents is a spy for the other side!

25

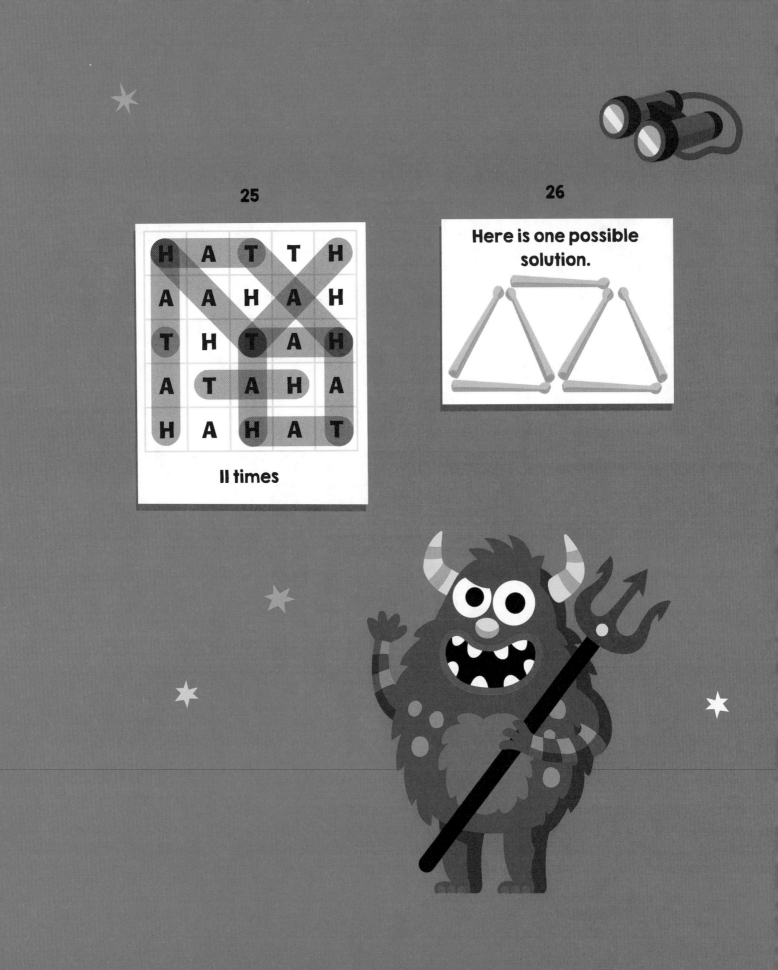

II times

26

Here is one possible solution.